MR. HOW DO YOU DO LEARNS TO PRAY

Written By Kelly Johnson
Illustrated by Jan Hamilton

10-25-15

Joan -
Enjoy journeying with Jesus in prayer He has so much to show you!
♡ Kelly Johnson

He loves you very much, as do I!
Jan Hamilton

innovo
PUBLISHING

Mr. How Do You Do is a children's series featuring personified birds in whimsical stories that captivate children of all ages and help them grow in a vibrant relationship with Jesus.

Published by
Innovo Publishing LLC
www.innovopublishing.com
1-888-546-2111

Providing Full-Service Publishing Services for
Christian Authors, Artists and Organizations: Books, eBooks,
Audiobooks, Music & Film

MR. HOW DO YOU DO LEARNS TO PRAY

Library of Congress Catalog Card Number: 20159-49022
ISBN 13: 978-1-61314-295-0

Cover Design & Interior Layout by Innovo Publishing LLC
Cover Art & Illustrations by Jan Hamilton

Printed in the United States of America
U.S. Printing History
First Edition: September 2015

Dedication

This book is dedicated in loving memory of my grandmothers,
Frances and Josephine, who intimately knew
the One they prayed to with faith-filled prayers.

Their lives of prayer shaped a daughter, Pauline,
and a son, Paul, whose prayer lives would ultimately
shape mine. Thanks, Mom and Daddy,
for always pointing me to Jesus!

Thank You, Jesus, for the legacy of prayer
that now allows me to share the gift with the world.
You are the Author and Perfecter of every story in my life.

ello! I'm Mr. How Do You Do.
Why, I am fine and how about you?

I've had the most amazing day, for
I've been learning
how to pray
P R A Y

I'd love to teach you.
Come with me.
It's really easy.
You will see.

At first I thought,
Oh me! Oh my!
Will my prayers ever reach the sky?

God is oh so high above, beyond the stars and Spaceeeeeeeeeeeee

But Jesus came down in His love
and now we're face-to-face.

I know He wants to live in me.
He wants to speak,
so listening's key.
Does He care what
I have to say?
Oh, dear Jesus, teach me
to pray.

all began with that simple request,
then
out flew a
robin with a
pretty red vest.

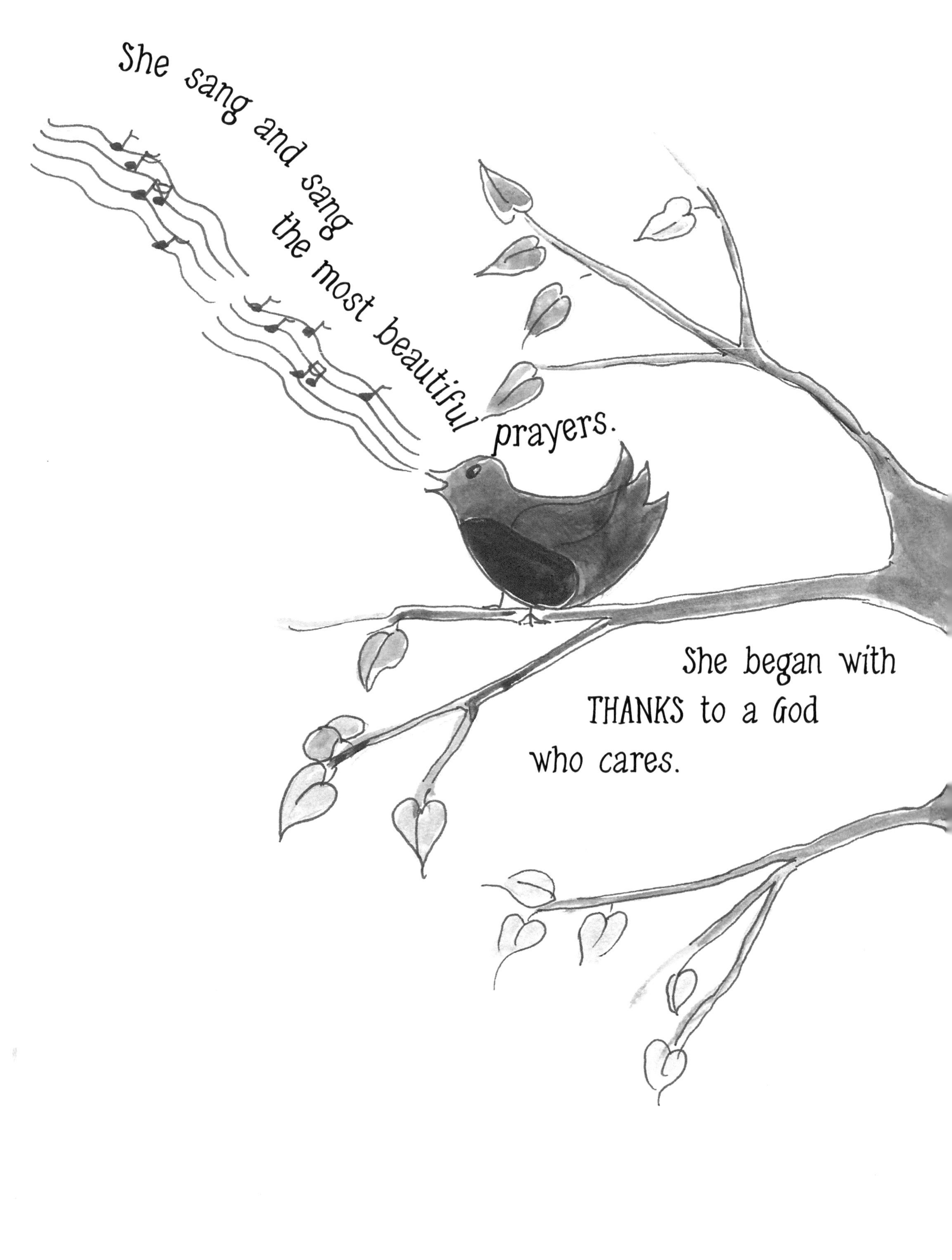
She sang and sang
the most beautiful prayers.
She began with
THANKS to a God
who cares.

She thanked Him for her vest because it kept her warm.

She
thanked
Him
for her nest where she
hid in a STORM.

he strangest of things, this was
eally absurd,
A
B
S
U
R
D
he talked to Him
like a friend,
as if He
heard.

I could see Ruby Robin had bee
praying fo
a while

She kne
He wa
listening
you could te
by her smile

Ruby realized prayer was
more than getting
a bunch of things.

Prayer was friendship with Jesus
and a time to
REST her wings.

At first Ruby asked,
"Jesus, why all
this pain?"

She knew His love,
and she hated to
complain.

Yes, Ruby had hard
times too, I saw
some missing
feathers . . .

But during those hard times, I knew
she'd found her greatest treasures.

You see, some days she'd sing loud,
look up, and pray.

But most days she'd bow low
and wait to hear Him say . . .

"I love you, dear one,
won't you come talk to Me?

And I'll talk to you,
now listen, you'll see . . ."

Ruby sat with Jesus and
He taught her how to pray.

She didn't learn to pray by studying
or taking lessons from Mr. Jay.

She just talked to Jesus throughout
each and every day.

o I thought if Ruby Robin
ould do this,

fter all,
she is just a bird,

ou and I can try it too,
nd see if we can
e heard.

I tried it just this morning; there's a smile
in my heart.
I'm only just
beginning
and what a place
to start.
I simply talked to Jesus;
I told Him I loved Him so . . .

nd then I tried to listen,

for I knew it would make me grow.

Prayer is just as easy
as conversation
with a friend.
There's talking
and listening,
yet with God
it doesn't end.

No wonder there was a big smile
on Ruby Robin's face!

Prayer for her was so much more
than simply saying "grace."

ell, thank you, Ruby Robin!
ou've taught us quite
a lot today.
nd now I'd like to
each you too . . .
ill you join me
s I pray?

Prayer for Kids
to pray out loud

Dear Jesus, thank You that
prayer is talking to You
from my heart.
I want to talk to You more, so this is just the start

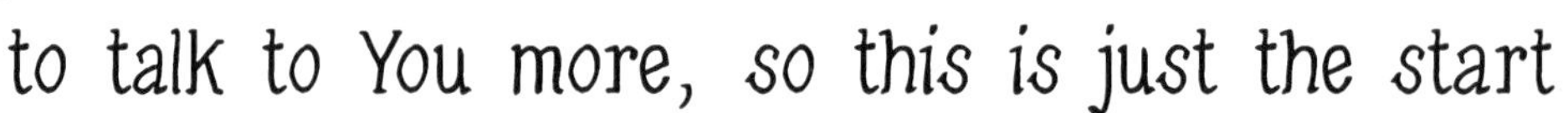

Help me to know that You are with me all through my day.
You don't need big grown-up words; You just want me to pray.

During the hard times, Jesus, I will listen to Your voice;
I know You're always with me and trusting is a choice.

I will be quiet enough to hear You; You want to speak to me.
I will not forget to thank You, for praising You is key.

Jesus, thank You I can talk to You when I'm big and when I'm sma
Thank You when I'm weak; You're the strongest One of all.

This is just the beginning; teach me more and more each day.
For I love You, precious Jesus, and I want to learn to pray.

Amen

Mr. How Do You Do tried to fill
the God-shaped hole in his heart
with many things,
but soon discovered
only **Jesus** could fill
that empty place.

Would you like to ask Jesus to fill your too?
Simply ask Him:
"Dear Jesus,
forgive my sin
and fill my . Because
of the , I give
my life to You."

Amen

Resource Page

Visit us at: mrhowdo.com for more family-friendly resources and additional titles in the MR. HOW DO YOU DO series.

An Important Note To Parents

r grown-ups and children alike, inviting Jesus into our hearts and being "born again" spiritually is the most im- rtant decision in life. So we've provided additional FREE resources on our website at mrhowdo.com to more fully scuss how to trust Jesus as your Savior and have a personal relationship with Him. These resources will help you k with your child about sin and how to be forgiven and reconciled to God forever through our Savior — JESUS.

also want you to know that although salvation (i.e., being born again spiritually and thus being reconciled with d for eternity) is a one-time event, Mr. How Do You Do will share his salvation experience at the end of each book the series. That's because we want everyone who reads these books to know about Jesus and how to be saved.

Mr. How Do You Do's

FREE Ten-Week Curriculum for Leaning How to Pray
for Parents, Grandparents, Teachers, and Children
DOWNLOAD YOUR FREE COPY NOW
mrhowdo.com

Enjoy More Books in The MR. HOW DO YOU DO series:

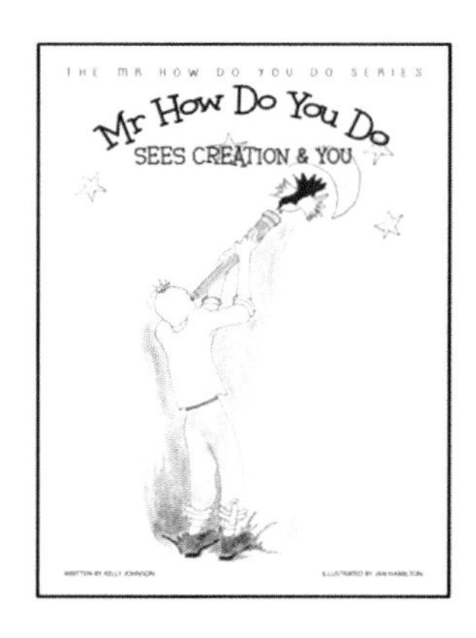

www.mrhowdo.com

CPSIA information can be obtained
at www.ICGtesting.com
Printed in the USA
LVIC04n1131091015
457223LV00001B/1
* 9 7 8 1 6 1 3 1 4 2 9 5 0 *